Young En...
Hand...

by Bob Symes

To S...

not all good wishes

Bob Symes

Acknowledgement:
Grateful thanks to David Somner, Basic Electronics
Guildford, Surrey

Safety notice:

For the safety of young engineers, adult supervision is always recommended. No liability whatsoever can be accepted by the publishers, author or illustrator in connection with any activities associated with this book, neither from any ideas arising from its subject matter.

First published November 1993.

Bright Books Limited, Great Sampford,
Essex, CB10 2RQ, England

ISBN 1-873967-08-X

Typeset by Set Two, Ely, Cambridgeshire

Printed in India by Thomson Press (India) Ltd

Contents

To would-be young engineers ....
a message from Bob Symes:

Everyone wanting to make something needs to know a little about the materials and processes they might wish to use. The one resource which you will need to use a lot of - and which marks out a true engineer - is ingenuity. Engineers are creative, inventive people who use their minds to put all manner of materials and machinery to good use. True engineers also find they have a great deal of fun in using their inventiveness: the act of creating new technology and making it work turns engineers (for the most part) into happy, satisfied people!

Handbooks for the qualified engineer are full of very precise facts. A handbook for ingenious young people seemed to me to be the best way to encourage would-be young engineers to explore their own creativity to the full. This book will not help you to design steam engines or computers, but it will open the door to the language and thinking of professional engineers. Lastly, do keep an eye on the pocket-money: don't let your ingenuity run away with you!

Bob Symes
(R A von Symes-Schutzmann, A.O.M., Comp. RAeS, President, Institute of Patentees and Inventors)

Section one: Power

The most easily available form of power is human power. Old-fashioned sewing-machines and spinning-wheels work on treadle power - foot-pedal power. Drills can be powered by hand, such as the drill and bit. The word 'power' means a useable form of energy. All energy costs something: the more highly it is packaged the more expensively it comes. Human power is paid for too, because nothing is free! Either you're going to get tired by applying your own power or you'll have to induce a friend by giving him something for his labour.

You could use a bike's transmission to the rear wheel (the chain) as a power source. You - or a friend! - could power a small generator; a fan; a water pump; a small lathe or even a grindstone, just by sitting and pedalling. The transmission of power comes through a belt drive.

A big wheel turns slowly with lots of power; a small wheel turns very fast with little power. A piece of spliced rope running where the tyre would be on the bike wheel will form your belt. The size of the second, grooved wheel, which is the 'driven' wheel, will depend upon what you are aiming to use the power for. For a fan, it could be a small wheel; for a pump, it would have to be much larger. As you will have to adapt the speed and power to your own final needs, you will in fact be designing a matched transmission - commonly called a gear-box - of your own.

You can drive very small generators and pumps from the wind power available to us all. Wind power by nature is quite moderate and cannot be relied upon as a constant source, so the cheapest way of using it is to drive a small generator and store the power in a rechargeable accumulator.

Small accumulators are usually sealed and look a little like ordinary batteries. You will certainly have heard of one type of accumulator: the rechargeable battery. These are known to engineers as nickel-cadmium accumulators or nicad cells. They store electricity because of the chemical properties of their cells. When electricity is demanded from them, the chemical action is reversed. This ability to reverse the

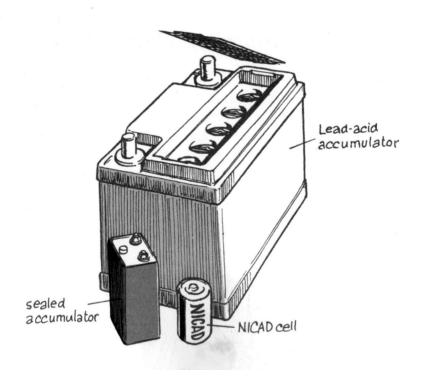

Lead-acid accumulator

sealed accumulator

NICAD cell

process in both directions makes them accumulators. A one-way production of electric energy can only happen in a conventional 'battery'.

Although it is possible to build an accumulator, it's a very messy affair and the young engineer would be advised to look out for a small, second-hand, sealed accumulator or use a rechargeable battery. Wind-driven generators and accumulators are used on yachts which are often left unattended for months. The wind generator charges the group of cells inside the accumulator with electricity for the lighting circuit.

Harnessing wind

To catch the wind, you can fix some slats from old Venetian blinds to the spokes of an old bike wheel. Rest the wheel in the front fork of an old bike frame. Make a vane to attach to the wheel so that the wheel will always face into the wind. If you're lucky you might

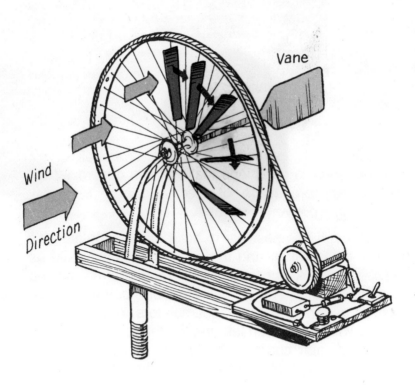

find an old wheel with a hub generator. If you do, you will not need to make your own transmission.

If you haven't managed to find a hub generator, then ask in a model shop for a small permanent magnet electric motor. Some motors are more efficient than others - ask the shop assistant for help in choosing the right one. Make yourself a transmission with the big wheel of your bike-windmill connected via a transmission belt to a small wheel fixed to the motor. The motor will now act as a generator. You may find the hole in the wheel is the wrong size to fix the wheel to the generator: if it's too small, open it out. If it's too big, you'll have to 'sleeve' it - fill out the space between the very small shaft and the big hole.

Electrically connect the generator to the accumulator via a 'gate circuit': a circuit which does not allow the power from the accumulator to drive the generator. Take a look at the gate circuit diagram below.

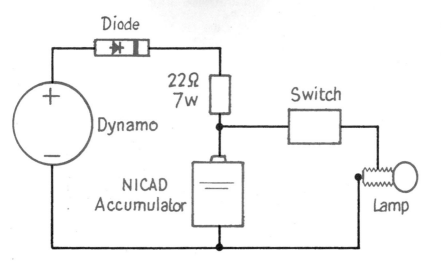

Small transistors or 'diodes', which operate like gates, will do the job. These can be obtained from good electronic spares shops where you may also find advice and help with any questions about the circuit.

The gate circuit allows the nicad accumulator to charge up to about 1.25 volts. Current can pass through the diode in one direction only and is limited to the correct level by the wire-wound resistor. It is important that the switch is left in the 'off' position during charging. The lamp can then be switched on whenever it is required. This is a simple circuit to keep costs to a minimum, and therefore needs a fairly brisk breeze to give good results. It does, though, give you a good insight into the way such systems work.

Make sure that your wind generator produces a higher voltage than your accumulator can deliver. To do this you need to measure the output of your wind generator with a small meter, which you can obtain inexpensively from an electronics shop.

The power that you use on a more day-to-day basis at your work-bench forms an important part of costing out your end products. When you are making something, you need to take into account all the costs involved - right down to the bag of sweets or can of fizzy you bought to pay for your friend's pedal-pushing!

Section two: Communications

For the engineer, it is useful to be able to communicate easily within the range of his own field of operation. Outside it, there are of course public telephones! Inside, though, it's much more fun to have your own private communications system, which can be made at very little cost.

Microphones, small speakers and buzzers are all available in shops today, as are walkie-talkie sets. Walkie-talkies need a special mention, because they use radio waves to send communications signals. Each person using a walkie-talkie takes up a certain amount of 'air space' in the range of frequencies available for this purpose. It is therefore necessary to have legal restrictions in terms of usage and transmission power. Too many users would crowd the airwaves and would halt the vital work of the emergency services (fire, ambulance and police) which also use these frequencies.

There are legal ways to communicate over the air, for example, through the CB (Citizens' Band). CB frequencies are grouped into 40 channels around the 27 MHz (twenty-seven Mega Hertz) wave band. There is a maximum power restriction of four Watts and you are legally required to purchase a licence to operate your CB radio set. These licences are available from Post Offices. The legal situation regarding low-powered walkie-talkie sets, such as can be found in toy shops, is a little confusing at present. It would be a good idea to obtain the latest information on regulations before purchasing walkie-talkie sets.

Microphones are much more straightforward! Airwaves hit the microphone in the form of air pressure produced by either speech or sound. The amount of electricity that is modulated (changed) or generated and becomes available is very small. To be useable it has to be made larger: it has to be amplified. The amplifier will make a useable amount of power available which can be either transmitted over long distances or can drive a loudspeaker. A loudspeaker is nothing more than a funnel-shaped cone being pushed backwards and forwards by a magnet, which gets its power from the amplifier.

Is there anybody there?

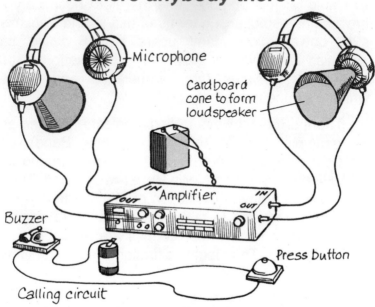

12

You can make yourself a very simple intercom. All the bits and pieces for an intercom can be bought, or you can use your ingenuity to make it yourself using two sets of old headphones. One end of each set of headphones could be used as a microphone and the other, with the aid of a large cardboard cone placed in the middle, could be the loudspeaker. You will need a calling circuit with a bell or a buzzer, to alert each other to incoming calls.

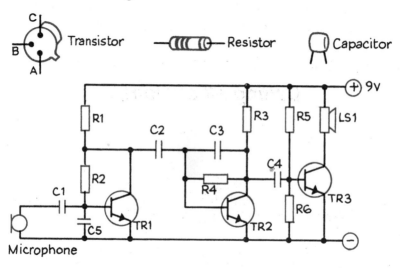

To build the amplifier, you will need a resistor, a capacitor and a transistor. All engineers have to take specialist advice at some point. In order to choose the right products from the wide range available, you will need the advice of a knowledgeable electronics shop assistant. When you have all the components you need, look at the diagram to get the connections right. Whenever working with electronic components, it is very important to connect them correctly to avoid damage.

The circuit diagrams in this book show some of the standard symbols representing various components. The weak signal from the microphone is amplified by the components in the circuit until it becomes strong enough to drive the loudspeaker. This then provides sound.

Electronics is becoming more advanced all the time and there are many ICs (integrated circuits, also sometimes called micro-chips) which contain all the components within the space of a postage stamp.

Calling all stations...

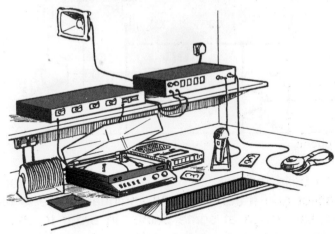

For your den or home, you can easily make your own mini broadcasting station by assembling a microphone, an old record player, and possibly a cassette recorder, connecting their output through a set of switches to a line with an amplifier and a loudspeaker. In professional recording studios, much larger versions of these switch combinations are called 'mixing desks'. Alternatively, you could easily operate without the extra switching, by using the volume controls on your equipment to fade music in and out through a loudspeaker.

You'll be able to select the output from any of the sources via your 'mixing desk', and feed them down the line to the loudspeaker. Friends and family can listen to your programmes, which will mix your chatter with music from the record player or the tapes. Remember that it takes time to load records and cassettes so always alternate between the sources - otherwise you'll have what is called in the broadcasting business: 'dead air'! Use a watch to make sure you get your timing right!

Safety first!

NEVER USE YOUR INGENUITY WITH THE MAINS: IT COULD LEAD TO YOUR LAST BROADCAST! Never overload plugs, or leave extension leads trailing around the house. Also remember that what may sound like a good programme to you may be annoying to neighbours and other people, so please keep the sound down!

Section three: Heating and Ventilating

The environment we live in may not always be ideally suited for work. Sometimes it's too hot; sometimes it's too cold. The builder provides us with a weather-proof place in which to live. But it is the engineer, using his ingenuity, who will make the place comfortable and pleasant to live and work in. The analysis of needs and the designing of equipment to cater for them is the job of the heating and ventilating engineer. The installation of the equipment, and its maintenance, is the job of a different kind of specialist: the plumber. Why not try analysing the heating and ventilating needs of your own space, whether it's a den or a shed or a tree-house, and designing some equipment to fulfil them.

Hot water from the sun

You may want warm water to wash your hands and you will not have access to mains electricity or gas to heat the water for you. Here's a challenge: design a solar heating system that really works. All you need is an old radiator from a scrap-yard and some black paint (or some black plastic hose); tin foil, and something which will act as a tank such as an old plastic bucket or wastepaper-bin.

As an engineer you will know how a thermo-syphon system works. Hot water is lighter than cold

Alternative system using black hose

water and therefore rises. If you have found an old radiator, paint it matt black all over. Place your radiator (or hose) on a backing of tin foil and put it in a sunny position. Now make a circuit between your radiator (or hose), and your storage tank, connecting at both top and bottom. Fill the system with cold water and make sure there are no air-locks as they'll stop the circulation. Purge the circuit of air by blowing water through until no bubbles come out. Now leave it to work on its own. You will find that the water in your storage tank will start getting warmer - much more so on a hot day! Nevertheless, this system gives you warm water for washing your hands fairly cheaply without draining domestic resources.

On a hot day, you will want to ventilate your space. It is worthwhile studying the air currents in your den by using a very small, light 'down' feather to watch how the air moves. You will find hot air rises to the ceiling, so to make your space more liveable-in you will have to let the hot air escape. Replacement air must not cause an unpleasant draught. You may find the simplest solution to ventilation is to open the window! Alternatively, this might not be the right solution for you because of outside traffic noise.

Scoop up the air!

How about making a a small fan or an air scoop?. A small fan could be easily made with a battery and a motor. An air scoop - such as are used on ships - could provide fresh air just where you need it: above your workbench. Fresh air can be ducted in trunking made of cardboard boxes to reach where it's needed; a toilet-roll tube would be the ideal outlet.

To make the scoop, make a hole in the side of an old bucket to fit a baked-bean tin. Connect the hole to more cans of the same width stuck together with carpet tape. Your engineering skills will tell you how solidly you will have to mount your cans! To make the scoop moveable into the wind, you will need to obtain a swivel fitting, similar to a rain-water or waste-water fitting, to fit your can. It shouldn't be too tight a fit or you will not be able to turn the can stack into the wind.

If you were to knock the bottom out of your bucket, the system would act as an air extractor unit to remove unwanted 'fumes'!

A swivelling connection (try a builders yard)

As all heating and ventilating engineers use pipework, you might like to know that the international code for pipe colouring is green for sea-water; blue for freshwater; black for soil and waste water; light grey for chemicals; red for fire installations; white for compressed air; oil is brown, and steam is aluminium. Very often, this colour code is painted in rings around the pipes, usually once in each visible run of pipe.

Section four: Movement

In any engineering works, however small, you may have to move products and information. Information can usually be dealt with by telecommunication. Products, on the other hand, may have to be handled. This is often both inconvenient and tedious, and a variety of product-handling systems have been introduced.

In large factories, overhead monorails move components through various work-stations, so that the right parts are always at hand. Where components have to be added, these too have to arrive at the work-station. They are often prepared in a batch, put in an open metal basket and delivered to the work-stations at the correct rate by a self-steering

robot tug. This is a tractor-type of vehicle which has a steering mechanism built into it. The steering recognises a painted line on the floor. It will move at a pre-programmed speed, recognise obstructions and allow no build-up of unwanted parts at work-stations.

Rails and pistons

You may think that you wouldn't be able to make good use of a component-moving system. Yet you'd be surprised how convenient a small model railway can be if several friends are working with you: you could make your own flow-line for assembly of anything which needs many small components.

Heavy items have to be lifted by cranes. Cranes often carry the letters SWL which stand for Safe Working Load. You may think that you don't yet need to come into contact with cranes, but if you help your parents with any car repairs you very quickly run into crane-size weights.

For lifting heavy equipment, hydraulic jacks are also useful. They are devices based on a cylinder, with a piston which carries the weight, and a small pump attached. Many strokes of the small pump will get the piston moving little by little, thereby producing enormous pressure. If you want to tilt small work-pieces without touching them you can make your own air-operated jack which could be as simple as a balloon-pump attached to a small balloon and as complicated as pumps and pistons with levers such as those provided in construction sets.

Similar types of hydraulic piston devices are used for splitting heavy logs.

Running on a tightrope

Can you make yourself an overhead monorail, which runs like a cable car? It's a clever form of communication and can be used to link your space or den and an outside place. Small containers sus-pended on a bogie, rather like that on a ski-lift, can be either pulled or projected along a taut rope or wire. Good design and engineering will prevent the contain-ers falling off. You can power the monorail with a battery and a small electric motor, geared to the right

speed. It will need quite some ingenuity to get the speed right, and the gear box you will have to design will certainly test your skills! And don't go 'over the top' with the design: over-engineering can be as bad as under-engineering!

Section five: Holding things together

One of the problems of designing a piece of equipment is how to make it easy to assemble and hold together during its intended life span. The carpenter has a simple answer: use a hammer and nails. The engineer has to do a lot more thinking.

If things have to be assembled and have to come apart for servicing, then a screw, a stud, a nut or a bolt may be necessary. Many engineers sitting at drawing boards forget that spanners are also a 'hidden component'. In a factory, things can be bolted together using specialised tools. But 'in the field', you have only to listen to the comments of the garage mechanic - or even your parents! - when trying to unbolt an inaccessible car part in a restricted space to see the trouble caused by a lack of forward thinking at the planning stage!

'Shrinks' and nuts

Bolts, nuts and studs are some of the most readily-available components for holding things together. At present, there are many different threads available from BA (British Association) to Whitworth, from Gas to metric. It is hoped that, by the time you become a professional engineer, the variety of threads will have shrunk to a manageable number. Mechanics will then no longer need their dreaded adjustable wrenches!

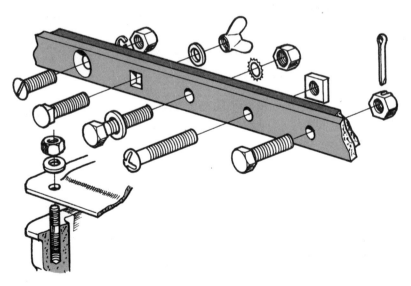

Bolts are metal bars with a thread and a hexagonal head on the end. They are fastened at the other end by a nut. A nut is a hexagonal piece of metal with a threaded hole matching the bolt.

A stud is a threaded bar which fits into a 'blind' hole (a hole which does not pierce the material), usually applied where it's impossible to fit a nut.

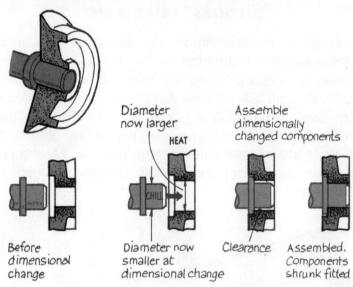

Prefabricated items which have to be assembled into a never-to-be-broken-up unit can be put together using other means. The simplest way is to shrink them together. The item to be shrunk has to be slightly chilled while the other piece has to be slightly warmed. The effect of the change in temperature between leaving one item in a pot of hand-hot water and the other in the fridge for 20 minutes is sufficient to get a very tight fit.

You can see how efficient this is by finding, say, a round plastic pen shaft. Make a hole slightly too small for it in another piece of plastic, and heat this in hot water while cooling the pen shaft in the fridge. When you put them together and wait for them to assume normal temperature, you will find they will not come apart! This is called a 'shrink fit'.

Beware: hot stuff!

Getting various metals to hold together is a process which can only be undertaken by the skilled professional and is not for the young engineer to try. Welding and other processes are most certainly dangerous, particularly to the eyes and hands. They can, however, be fascinating to watch, provided you have been equipped by a professional welder with all the necessary safety and eye-protection gear, and watch from the distance which he or she dictates.

Metals which are similar can be welded together. The process of welding is to melt a little of each of the

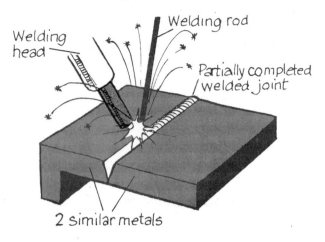

Welding rod

Welding head

Partially completed welded joint

2 similar metals

27

parts and fill the gap with similar material provided in the shape of a rod. Welding can be done electrically or by gas, or with a chemical process. All welding requires great professional skill and is dangerous. Machine welding uses expensive precision equipment.

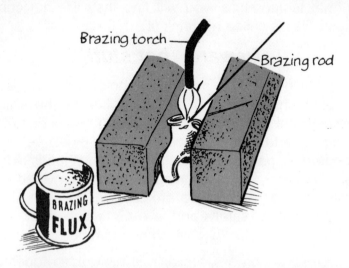

Brazing torch — Brazing rod

BRAZING FLUX

Holding dissimilar metals together requires less heat and uses a process called brazing. A brass rod is used as a filler; this process can be done by gas or with a specially-adapted electrical tool. This is a skill which can be acquired by adults used to handing hot materials. Silver soldering requires even less heat and uses a silver rod and a special flux.

Under supervised conditions at school, you may have the opportunity to try soft soldering, again, provided that you are equipped with the relevant safety gear. Even with soft soldering, the temperatures involved produce dangerous and painful burns.

Making a soft-soldered joint involves the use of an electric soldering-iron of the right temperature. Both work-pieces have to be hot and the solder run sparingly in the gap between them. Successful soldering depends upon the work being absolutely clean and free from fat or grease, the soldering-iron being clean, and the right commercial flux applied.

Soft solder can break down under certain temperature conditions. If you wish to join for example non-mains low-tension (or low-voltage) audio wires together, use small plastic terminal blocks. They cost very little to buy. Remember NEVER to tamper with mains electricity or electrical cables!

All stuck up ...

In recent years the armoury of the engineer has been enhanced by modern glues. First you must understand how the gluing process works. Gluing simply excludes the air between two pieces of work

and lets air pressure hold them together at a rate of one kilogramme per square centimetre. You can test this very simply by putting two sheets of shiny plastic together with a drop of water between them. Now try to separate them!

Professional engineers' glue is different. It operates only when the air is removed from the glue itself: this means it is 'anaerobic'. This type of glue sets fairly fast and will hold pieces together under normal temperatures. It is very convenient and has been used in processes as large as fitting locomotive tyres to wheels. This glue is sold domestically as 'instant' glue and has even been used medically. It is, however, dangerous to handle. If you feel you may need to use this type of glue, ask for adult supervision, and wear goggles and protective gloves and clothing.

Section six:
Cost-Counting

There's an old saying: you can turn an engineer into a manager but you can't turn a manager into an engineer! Any engineer worth his/her salt has to manage and cost out their own knowledge, resources, and time, before putting forward a design of any kind. You might not think this applies to you as yet, but it is better to adjust your thinking sooner rather than later. Without proper design-costing even the most professional engineer will appear stupid if costs eventually rise well above the level of the value of the end product! If you want to 'market' your end products to family and friends, you too will have to make sure your don't end up out-of-pocket!

Very few young engineers realise that their own time is valuable and has to be considered as part of the 'primary costing'. The next most important factor is the final and total cost of the raw materials. Add to this a few costs which you might not have considered, such as machining, cleaning, tidying up and painting ready for presentation, and you can begin to see why accurate costing is important.

Let's go one stage deeper. Every time you use a drill, you should think about the cost of re-sharpening it or replacing it. Every time you use an electrical tool, you have to bear in mind that it will eventually wear out and have to be replaced. Every time you go shopping for spare bits and bobs you are actually costing your product money. Every phone call and every letter has to be included in your final costing. The safety equipment - be it goggles, insulating material or whatever - has to be costed-in.

One category of costing which the young engineer does not yet have to consider is 'overheads'. Normally you live at home and have no travelling expenses to your place of engineering activity. Luckily you probably won't have to produce profits either just yet! Nevertheless, any engineering activity is a managerial one, and it is well worth starting to think in terms of costing right at the beginning. You can then decide whether it is worth your while to make something or to buy it 'off the shelf'.

Costing, however, should not inhibit your ideas; it should simply make you aware that everything has a price - most of all, you! With costing in mind, though, you'll be able to discuss all your ideas with a self-confidence that is the stock-in-trade of any good engineer.

Glossary

Accumulator
A device which STORES electricity through a chemical process which can be reversed to RELEASE electricity on demand.

Adjustable Wrench
A spanner which can be adjusted to a variety of widths in the gap in which it grasps a nut.

Amateur
Someone not professionally trained, or who 'dabbles' for fun in a particular activity.

Amplifier
Electrical components put together to enlarge a small electrical current and to thereby give greater power, as in a radio or tape recorder.

Amp (A)
Unit of quantity of electric flow named after French physicist, André Ampère. Ampère's main contribution to science was the discovery and development of electromagnetism.

Anaerobic
Without air (in this case oxygen).

Baffle
Curtain or small wall making air currents and/or sounds travel in a different direction.

Battery
A series of cells PRODUCING electricity by chemical means; also means a group of electrical storage cells.

Block Diagram
Drawing of component parts with their names and functions written into small rectangular blocks without giving the actual electrical circuit.

Bogie
A small truck with several axles used to carry a heavy load.

Brass
A mixture of copper and zinc.

Brazing
Method of joining dissimilar metals with brass rods.

C
Short symbol for 'Cell'

Capacitor
Electric component which has two 'legs' and is capable of storing electrical charge. These components are used in timing, audio and smoothing circuits. Electrolytic capacitors must be connected into a circuit with care as they have '+' and '-' terminals.

Chip
Slang term for integrated circuit.

Circuit
Route of wires to show how components are linked.

Component
Part of; separate but necessary piece.

Costing
Assessment of monies needed.

Current
Rate of flow of electricity.

Diode
Electronic component which has two 'legs' and allows current to flow in one direction only.

Electrolyte
Type of fluid which acts as a carrier for electricity, used particularly in electric cells and batteries.

Electronic
Adjective used to describe something in which the behaviour of electrons (particles of electricity) is controlled by electrical means (not by a mechanical device).

Flow-Line
A way of making products in sequence with several separate assemblies performed by different people, also known as production line.

Flux
Material which excludes oxygen and makes soldering possible.

Gas threads
Threads designed for use with gas fittings and equipment.

Hertz (Hz)
Unit of frequency of radio waves named after German scientist Heinrich Hertz. Hertz was the first to demonstrate the production and reception of radio waves.

Insulating tape
Special sticky tape used as a temporary, 'stop-gap' measure to wrap around low-voltage wires, giving a small amount of protection against short-circuit. Insulating tape should NOT be used for joining wires, nor as a easy or long-term solution to a wiring problem.

Integrated circuit (IC)
Electronic component which has several 'legs' (perhaps 14 or more) and contains complete circuits in a very compact form. ICs are sometimes called chips or microchips.

Kilo- (k)
A thousand times a particular measure.

Leg
Slang term for short metal rods on electric or electronic components to which connecting wires must be fixed.

Low-tension
An alternative, more 'professional' term for low-voltage.

Milli- (m)
One-thousandth of a particular measure.

Mega- (M)
A million times a particular measure.

Micro- (μ)
A millionth of a particular measure.

Micro-chip
Very small electronic circuit formed on small plate with connectors. (See Integrated Circuit above.)

Modulate
To change, modify.

Ω Ohm
Unit of electrical resistance named after the German physicist Georg Simon Ohm, who discovered the relationship between resistance, power and electrical pressure, called Ohm's law.

Over-engineering
Engineering design more complicated than necessary.

Permanent magnet motor
A motor where the magnetic field is provided by a block of permanently magnetic material.

Prefabricated
Parts put together into a small assembly being joined to make a more complete piece.

Preprogrammed
Certain behaviour or demands built in.

Purge
Drive out , remove by force.

Resistor
Electric component which has two 'legs' and restricts the flow of current in a circuit. They are often coded with coloured bands relating to the reistance value.

Robot tugs
Small automatically guided tractors.

Shrink fit
Fitting a part into another by heating the outside and chilling the inside material. A tight, strong fit.

Sleeve
A round piece of metal fitted to a shaft to make it larger.

Soft Solder
Mixture of lead and tin that melts at low temperature.

Soldering
Joining metals at low temperature.

SPST
Single pole, single throw switch.

Thermo-syphon
System using the lighter weight of warm liquids to circulate liquids (as in some radiators and car cooling systems), not using a pump.

Thread
Turns of grooves and hills on a bolt.

Transistor
Electronic component which has three 'legs' and enables a small circuit, applied to the base terminal, to control larger currents flowing between the emitter and collector terminals. Transistors are used in many applications where electronic control is required, such as sensing- and switching-circuits; they are also used in amplifiers.

Volt (V)
Unit which measures the force or 'potential' of an electric current, named after Italian scientist Alessandro Volta. Volta invented the electric cell, the fore-runner of today's batteries.

Watt (W)

Basic unit of power. Used in mechanical engineering before its application to electricity. Now used to measure the power produced or consumed by an electrical circuit. Named after James Watt, inventor of the first effective steam engine.

Welding

Melting metals and joining them, with similar metal as a filler, at around 1,500 degrees.

Whitworth

In 1841, Sir Joseph Whitworth, originally a skilled craftsman and machine-tool maker, presented ideas for the standardisation of screw threads to the Institute of Civil Engineers. His threads brought order to the chaos in Victorian engineering at the time and are still with us today.

Enjoy Engineering!

This section will give you useful names and addresses from which you can really begin to enjoy the world of engineering to the full - and it's a very full world to enjoy, with many, many different branches from mechanics to genetics! There are clubs to join and competitions to take part in. And if you think you've a future as a professional engineer, there is information to be had on all the options available to you. Enjoy engineering!

CLUBS WORTH INVESTIGATING:

There are Young Engineers' clubs in some 400 schools around Britain, with a membership of around 8,000. The clubs aim to encourage 11-18 year olds to enjoy engineering as a pastime and as a potential career. They also have a national awards scheme with major prizes to be won, and their own magazine. For more information contact:

The National Director, Young Engineers
Headquarters, University of Surrey,
Guildford GU2 5XH. Tel: 0483 509349

Youth section of the British Association for the Advancement of Science. You can join as an individual member or through a school; BAYS clubs are located in many major towns and cities throughout the UK. BAYS covers all branches of science and organises special events for its members throughout the year including the BAYSDAYS at science and technology museums throughout the country. BAYS also runs an awards scheme for young scientists. For details of membership and activities contact:

The Membership Department, BAYS, Fortress House, 23 Savile Row, London W1X 1AB. Telephone: 071- 494 3326.

COMPETITIONS:

The Young Engineers for Britain Competition

Have you ever wanted to invent something? If you can turn your bright ideas into reality, you could enter one of the best-known competitions of its kind in the UK: The Young Engineers for Britain Competition, sponsored annually by The Engineering Council. Open to young engineers from 11-19 years of age, it has already launched a number of successful inventions from a navigating light system for rally drivers to an alarm device for children in danger. Litter collecting machines and safety irons have also been among the winners!

Regional finals are held in the summer with the national final each autumn. The winner receives a trophy and a substantial financial reward: your school will also benefit from your winning! Special prizes are also awarded for categories from the environment to electronics.

There are four age groups, and both individual and group entries are accepted. Marks are awarded for originality and enterprise, engineering and design skill, the application of scientific principles, and the overall presentation of the projects. Other factors such as marketability and economic and social usefulness are also considered. For further details contact :

The Young Engineers for Britain Competition, The Engineering Council, 10 Maltravers Street, London WC2R 3ER. Telephone: 071-240 7891.

And don't forget the awards run by the Young Engineers' clubs and by BAYS!

FOR THE FUTURE:

Want to know what the future could hold? Then here's a Freephone telephone number for you to ring to find out about a future in one of the many branches of engineering:

0800 282 167.

Free booklets are available on the different branches of engineering, in addition to careers advice. Staff at the Engineering Training Authority can also put you in touch with other organisations in specialist fields. Contact address:

Engineering Training Authority, Vector House 41 Clarendon Road, Watford, WD1 1HS.

Freephone: 0800 282 167.

PATENT PENDING!

If you find you have had a real brainwave, and you think you have come up with an idea worth selling, then it's wise to get immediate advice on patents. The Institute of Patentees and Inventors is a forum for inventors to share experiences and provides a voice for those embarking on the process of patenting new products and technologies.

The Institute has an active membership and welcomes enquiries from inventors of all ages. The address is:

The Secretary, Institute of Patentees and Inventors, Suite 505a, Triumph House, 189 Regent Street, London W1R 7WF. Tel: 071-242 7812.

If you would like to make contact with me personally, I would be pleased to hear from you. You can write to me through the Institute.

BOB SYMES

About the author ...

Bob Symes is one of Britain's best-loved TV science presenters. Having been a producer of BBC1's 'Tomorrow's World' science magazine programme for 20 years, Bob eventually went 'front on camera' and now presents a regular slot on new inventions under the heading 'Patent Pending'.

In addition to his 'Tomorrow's World' activities, Bob Symes broadcasts regularly on local, national and international radio and on television networks in Europe. He has produced and presented a highly successful set of TV science programmes for children entitled 'Bob's Your Uncle' which continue to run on The Children's Channel, and has also presented many television programmes on his other 'passions': railways and food!

Bob Symes is also an inventor of several industrial and commercial products and is President of the Institute of Patentees and Inventors.

His first children's book, 'Crikey! It Works', was published by Bright Books Ltd in March 1992 and continues to be used in both homes and classrooms across the country.

Also by Bob Symes .....

'Crikey! It Works'

Packed full of know-how for young inventors to try. Contains 'Inventamaniac Challenges' and information on the four basic topics of mechanics, air, water, and electricity. The main points on each topic are highlighted using easily-accessible domestic objects from toilets to toy 'planes! Useable both at home and in the classroom. CONTAINS SAFETY CODE FOR YOUNG INVENTORS.

Price: £ 3.99

Suitable for the 7-13 age range.

Paperback; full colour, 32 pages.

ISBN: 1-873967-01-2.

Available in libraries, at good bookshops or direct from the publisher. For direct orders, please send a cheque or postal order for £3.99 made payable to Bright Books Ltd to:

Consumer Orders Department, Bright Books Ltd, Carpenters, Great Sampford, Saffron Walden, Essex CB10 2RQ.

Other titles from Bright Books:

'Mars and Back'

by Andrew Read

An introduction to computer programming, a space-flight simulator and a computer game all rolled into one! For all machines using Microsoft Basic. Age range: 8-14 years. Publication: autumn 1993. Paperback.

Price: £2.25. ISBN 1-873967-09-8.

'NatureWatch by the Roadside'

Ideal for long car, bus or coach journeys all year round. Brightly illustrated, this book comes with its own national wildlife survey sheet from WATCH. For 6-10 year olds; includes green country code.

Price: £2.99. ISBN 1-873967-02-2.

'Say Hello on the Beach'

Say 'Hello' to new friends on the holiday beach in French, German, Spanish and Italian with this colourful, instant holiday-talk book. Age range 7-12 years. Includes contacts page for keeping new friends' names and addresses.

Price: £2.99 paperback; £4.99 hardback.

ISBNs: 1-873967- 03-9 (paper) -05-5 (hard)

Stories from the pen of Barbara Kennett:

Billy Fleet on the trail of ....

'Dream Drops' and 'Night Riders'

Two exciting stories for children of the 'nineties. London reporter-mouse Billy Fleet aims to crack crime and beat the bad guys on his newspaper's territory. In 'Dream Drops', Billy investigates drugged sweets being handed round in the local mouse playground. In 'Night Riders', Billy's own nephew gets caught up in theft and 'joy-riding'.   Suitable for 8-11 year olds.

Price: £2.25 each. ISBNs: 1-873967-06-3/-07-1

'Hero's Squadron'

A fast-moving, Euro-travelling adventure story for 8-11 year olds. Hero is a lame pigeon who flies with his 'squadron' on a desperate mission to track down their friend, green inventor Professor Boris Gentil.

Price: £2.25. ISBN: 1-873967-00-4.

'Mealtime Around the World'

Come travelling around the world at mealtime with UNICEF. A gift book for 4-6 year olds; proceeds aid UNICEF's international relief and development work. Hardback.

Price: £4.25; ISBN 1-873967-04-7.